To: Stanley M[illegible]
with best wishes

A. Cressy Morrison

*Man Does Not Stand Alone*

# MAN DOES NOT STAND ALONE

*By*

## A. CRESSY MORRISON

NEW YORK

Fleming H. Revell Company

LONDON AND EDINBURGH

New York: 158 Fifth Avenue
London: 99 Anerley Road

*By permission, I gratefully dedicate this book to* NORMAN VINCENT PEALE, D.D., *pastor of the Marble Collegiate Church of the City of New York, to whom the basic purpose of the book was submitted. It was because of his favorable comment and suggestion that the author was encouraged to prepare the material for publication.*

## NOTE

Because of an increased demand for this volume, as a result of the publication of a condensation in *The Reader's Digest* for December, 1946, this revised edition has been prepared.

This work attempts a review of the scientific evidence of the existence of a Supreme Intelligence, and the title was chosen as a challenge to the conclusion of Julian Huxley in his book *Man Stands Alone*. All parallel facts presented are pure coincidence.

*New York, N. Y.* A. C. M.

# The Reason Why

THE GOLDEN AGE of the natural philosopher reached its climax between 1820 and 1850. He sought evidence of the existence of definite design in creation by demonstrating the wonders of nature. He called attention to the ingenuity of the construction of the human eye with its telescopic and microscopic adjustments. He noted the wonderful flexibility and adjustability of the human joints. He marveled at the mysteries of reproduction and all the refinements and precision of the instrumentalities through which man and every living thing carried forward its life. He pointed out the unique chemical processes of living things, such as digestion and assimilation of food. Indeed, all the activities of nature were reviewed. Seen through the eye of his pious philosophy, these facts were to him conclusive evidences of the existence of design in nature, and, consequently, of a Designer. Paley used as an illustration the effect upon him of finding a watch in a pathway. Its mechanism was far less wonderful than many other evidences of design in nature. This led him to call attention to the fact that such an object would, however, convince the most skeptical of the evidences of an intellectual process applied to mechanics. He added that were this watch endowed with the power to bring into existence other watches, it would be a no greater marvel than the reproduction of man and animals. So far-reaching and so convincing was this process of reasoning that the sum of $48,000 was left to the Royal Society of Great Britain for an investigation in the various fields of science which would conclusively demonstrate the existence of God. The result was some twelve volumes written by members of the Royal Society and others. These studies brought forward with apparent conclusiveness the evidence of design, and demonstrated to the philosophers of that period the existence of a Supreme Being.

With the advent of Darwin, there entered into the thoughts of mankind a new conception—"the survival of the fittest" and the evolution of man. Darwin's comprehensive study and the vast number of sustaining facts which he brought to support his thesis carried conviction. To this day, his massing of evidence and the subsequent facts developed by his successors have sustained the theory of evolution and carried it far beyond Darwin's demonstrations. It is over eighty years since Darwin, and knowledge has developed enormously. While Darwin's theories stand as a rock of incredible strength, there is now being disclosed to the philosophic world a large number of demonstrable facts which carry us to other possible final conclusions. The modern science of genetics raises questions it is difficult to answer, and other new discoveries leave his work as only a great step in the advance of philosophic thought. Without detracting from either the accuracy of his deductions or the greatness of Darwin's work, no one can now conclude, as did Haeckel, that if given water, chemicals, and time, he could create a man.

Some of the followers of Darwin carried his deductions to the extreme of materialistic atheism. Those who felt the inspiration of belief in a Supreme Intelligence and a purpose in all things took the other extreme, and while attacking the atheistic attitude, also denied the facts of evolution. Today no such vigorous position need be taken by either the evolutionist or the religious minded, for science now has brought to light facts which go far to remove the apparent differences and enlighten both.

Curiously enough, the new discoveries and wider opportunities for investigation are bringing to life the conclusions of the natural philosophers which were completely eclipsed by the advent of Darwin's work. The sound arguments which showed the adaptation of man to nature should now be followed by a renewed investigation of the evidences of the adaptation of nature to man, which during the past eighty years has been relatively neglected. It is my purpose to bring to the attention of thinking people the facts now demonstrable which tend to sustain a belief in this adaptation and indicate its purpose.

The existence of a Supreme Being is demonstrated by infinite adjustments, without which life itself would be impossible. Man's presence on earth and the magnificent demonstrations of his intellect are a part of a program being carried out by the Supreme Intelligence. To quote Osborn, "Of all the incomprehensible things in the universe, man stands in the front rank, and of all the incomprehensible things in man, the supreme difficulty centers in the human brain, intelligence, memory, aspirations, power of discovery, research and the conquest of obstacles." It is the author's belief that the reader of this very brief summary of scientific truth will conclude that the enormous gap between man's surprising brain and all other living things is less "incomprehensible" than Osborn supposed at his time of writing.

The unknown increases in arithmetical progression as each unit of knowledge is acquired by man. But the breaking of Dalton's atom, which was regarded as a miniature building brick, into a constellation composed of a nucleus and flying electrons like planets, has opened up space for a radically changed conception of the universe and of reality. The deadly uniformity of discrete atoms no longer holds the imagination to the material, and the new knowledge leaves room for an effective intelligence behind the phenomena of nature.

This is a light in the vast mystery that at present surrounds the apparently unknowable which may lead us to a recognition of a universal and Supreme Intelligence.

# Contents

# I

## Our Unique World

SUPPOSE you take ten pennies and mark them from 1 to 10. Put them in your pocket and give them a good shake. Now try to draw them out in sequence from 1 to 10, putting each coin back in your pocket after each draw.

Your chance of drawing No. 1 is 1 to 10. Your chance of drawing 1 and 2 in succession would be 1 in 100. Your chance of drawing 1, 2, and 3 in succession would be one in a thousand. Your chance of drawing 1, 2, 3, and 4 in succession would be one in 10,000 and so on, until your chance of drawing from No. 1 to No. 10 in succession would reach the unbelievable figure of one chance in 10 billion.

The object in dealing with so simple a problem is to show how enormously figures multiply against chance.

So many essential conditions are necessary for life to exist on our earth that it is mathematically impossible that all of them could exist in proper relationship by chance on any one earth at one time. Therefore, there must be in nature some form of intelligent direction. If this be true, then there must be a purpose.

The object of this book is to point out some of these marvelous adjustments and suggest the purpose underlying the existence of man. Let us examine the surprising facts.

Some astronomers tell us that the chance of two stars passing sufficiently near to each other to develop a pulsating and destructive tide is in the order of millions and that a collision would be so rare that it is beyond calculation. Nevertheless, one of the astronomical theories is that at some time, let us say two billion years ago, a star did pass near enough to our sun to raise terrific tides and throw out into space those objects we know as the planets, which appear vast to us but are insignificant astronomically. Among those masses drawn out was that wisp of cosmos which became what we call the earth. It is a body of no importance astronomically, yet it may be demonstrated that it is the *most* important body so far known to us.

We must presume that the earth is composed of some of the elements which are to be found in the sun and none other. These elements are apportioned on earth in certain percentages, which, so far as the surface is concerned, have been fairly well ascertained. The bulk of the earth is now reduced to very permanent dimensions and its mass has been determined. Its speed in its orbit around the sun is extremely constant. Its rotation on its axis is determined so accurately that a variation of a second in a century would upset astronomical calculations. It is accompanied by a satellite known as the moon, whose motions are determined and whose sequence of variations repeat themselves every 18⅓ years. Had the bulk of the earth been greater or less, or had its speed been different, it would have been farther from or nearer to the sun, and this different condition would have profoundly affected life of all kinds, including man. So profoundly indeed, that had this earth varied in either respect to any marked degree, life as we know it could not have existed. Of all the planets, the earth is, so far as we now know, the only one whose relation to the sun makes our sort of life possible.

Mercury, because of astronomical laws, turns only one side to the sun, rotating on its axis only once in its complete revolution of the sun—Mercury's year. In consequence, one side of Mercury must be a desert furnace and the other frigid. Its mass and gravity are so small that all traces of an atmosphere seem to have escaped. If any atmosphere does remain, it is tearing in unbelievable tornadoes from one side of the planet to the other. Venus is a mystery, with dense vapor for atmosphere, and it is demonstrated to be absolutely uninhabitable by any known living thing. Mars is the one exception and may bear life like ours, either in its beginnings or on the point of extinction. But life on Mars must be dependent upon other gases than oxygen, and especially hydrogen; as they seem to have escaped. There can be no water on Mars. Its temperature averages too low for vegetation as we know it. The moon could not hold an atmosphere and is now absolutely uninhabitable. During its night it is extremely cold, and during its long day it is a very hot cinder. The other planets are too far from the sun for life to be established, and because of other insuperable difficulties cannot support life in any form. It is now generally agreed that there has never been, and can never be, life in any known form on any planet except our earth. Therefore, we have in the very beginning as a home for human beings a little planet which, after a series of vicissitudes during two or more billion years, has become a suitable place for the existence of plant and animal life, of which we find the crowning achievement to be man.

The earth rotates on its axis in twenty-four hours or at the rate of about one thousand miles an hour. Suppose it turned at the rate of a hundred miles an hour. Why not? Our days and nights would then be ten times as long as now. The hot sun of summer would then burn up our vegetation each long day and every sprout would freeze in such a night. The sun, the source of all life, has a surface temperature of 12,000 degrees Fahrenheit, and our earth is just far enough away so that this "eternal fire" warms us just enough and not too much. It is marvelously stable, and during millions of years has varied so little that life as we know it has survived. If the temperature on earth had changed so much as fifty degrees on the average for a single year, all vegetation would be dead and man with it, roasted or frozen. The earth travels around the sun at the rate of eighteen miles each second. If the rate of revolution had been, say, six miles or forty miles each second, we would be too far from or too close to the sun for our form of life to exist.

Stars vary in size, as we all know. One is so large

that if it were our sun, the orbit of the earth would be millions of miles inside its surface. Stars vary in the type of radiation. Many of their rays would be deadly to every known form of life. The intensity and volume of this radiation is anywhere from less than that of our sun to ten thousand times as great. If our sun gave off only one-half of its present radiation, we would freeze, and if it gave half as much more, we would have been reduced to dust long ago if we had ever been born as a protoplasmic spark of life. So our sun is about right for our life among millions of others which are not.

The earth is tilted at an angle of twenty-three degrees. This gives us our seasons. If it had not been tilted, the poles would be in eternal twilight. The water vapor from the ocean would move north and south, piling up continents of ice and leaving possibly a desert between the equator and the ice. Glacial rivers would erode and roar through canyons into the salt-covered bed of the ocean to form temporary pools of brine. The weight of the unbelievably vast mass of ice would depress the poles, causing our equator to bulge or erupt or at least show the need of a new waistline belt. The lowering of the ocean would expose vast new land areas and diminish the rainfall in all parts of the world, with fearful results.

We seldom realize that all life is confined to the space between the snow of the mountain tops and the heat of the earth's interior. This narrow stratum as compared with the diameter of the earth is but one half the thickness of one leaf of a thousand-page book.

The history of all creatures is written on this tissue-thin surface. If all the air was liquefied it would cover the earth to a depth of thirty-five feet or one part in six hundred thousand of the distance to the earth's center, a close adjustment!

The moon is 240,000 miles away, and the tides twice a day are usually a gentle reminder of its presence. Tides of the ocean run as high as sixty feet in some places, and even the crust of the earth is twice a day bent outward several inches by the moon's attraction. All seems so regular that we do not grasp to any degree the vast power that lifts the whole area of the ocean several feet and bends the crust of the earth, seemingly so solid. Mars has a moon—a little one—only six thousand miles away from it. If our moon was, say, fifty thousand miles away instead of its present respectable distance, our tides would be so enormous that twice a day all the lowland of all the continents would be submerged by a rush of water so enormous that even the mountains would soon be eroded away, and probably no continent could have risen from the depths fast enough to exist today. The earth would crack with the turmoil and the tides in the air would create daily hurricanes.

If the continents were washed away, the average depth of water over the whole earth would be about a mile and a half and life could not exist except perhaps in the abysmal depth of the ocean, where it would feed upon itself till extinct. Science seems to sustain the theory that this condition did exist during the general chaos before the earth solidified. By well recognized laws, the very tides pushed the moon farther and farther away and at the same time slowed the rotation of the earth from less than a six-hour day to one of twenty-four. So the gentle moon has now become the lover's delight and is in splendid adjustment, which promises to remain safe for a billion years or so. The same astronomers also believe that far in the future, by the same astronomical laws, the moon will return to the earth, burst when close enough and glorify our dead world with rings like those of Saturn.

Out of a chaotic mixture of the elements torn from the sun at twelve thousand degrees temperature, and thrown at every conceivable velocity into limitless space, has come our solar system. To chaos has come order so exact that the place any part will occupy at any time can be predicted to the second. The balance is so perfect that it has not varied in a billion years and points to eternity. All this through the reign of law. By this same law the established order as we see it in the solar system is repeated elsewhere.

# II

## *Atmosphere and Ocean*

SSUMING that present scientific conclusions may be erroneous and thus subject to some future change, still, the facts about to be presented in simple approximations for clarity's sake are in harmony with present knowledge, and it is improbable that any scientific modification will disturb the basic adjustments which will now be pointed out.

If it is true that the temperature of the earth at the time of its separation from the sun was about 12,000 degrees, or that of the surface of the sun, then all the elements were free and therefore no chemical combination of importance could exist. Gradually, as the earth, or earth-forming fragments, cooled, combinations would take place and a nucleus of the world as we know it was formed. Oxygen and hydrogen could not combine until the temperature was reduced to 4000 degrees Fahrenheit. At this point these elements would rush together and form water. What we know as the atmosphere of the earth must have been enormous at that time. All the oceans were in the sky and all those elements not combined were in the air as gases. Water, having formed in the outer atmosphere, fell toward the earth but could not reach it, as the temperature near the earth was higher than it was thousands of miles out. Of course, the time came when the deluge would reach the earth only to fly up again as steam. With whole oceans in the air, floods that would result as cooling progressed are beyond calculation. Upheaval and erosion rivaled each other and a condition of chaos beyond all comprehension existed for millions of years. In this inconceivable confusion, oxygen combined with nearly all the substances of the earth's crust. It also combined with all the hydrogen with which it came in contact and thus formed the ocean. Vast quantities of hydrogen must have escaped the attraction of the earth's gravity before the earth cooled. Otherwise, the mass of water would now have been so great as to bury the land miles deep. Perhaps a billion years ago things calmed down and settled themselves, thus forming the solid earth, the oceans, and the atmosphere—the residue we call air. The combination of all the elements was so complete that what was left, the air, consisting mainly of oxygen and nitrogen, amounts to considerably less than one part in many millions of the mass of the earth. Why was it not all absorbed or why was it not an unbelievably larger proportion? In either case, man as such could not exist, or if existence were possible under thousands of pounds of pressure per square inch, it is impossible that he could have evolved as man.

Without pressing this matter further, it is at least extraordinary that in this adjustment of nature there should have been such exquisite nicety. For, had the crust of the earth been ten feet thicker, there would be no oxygen, without which animal life is impossible; and had the ocean been a few feet deeper, carbon dioxide and oxygen would have been absorbed and vegetable life on the surface of the land could not exist. There is a possibility that practically all the oxygen was taken up by the crust of the earth and the seven seas and that the advent of all oxygen-breathing animals had to await the growths of plants which release oxygen. Careful calculation seems to make this source of the oxygen we breathe possible, but, whatever its source, the quantity is exactly adjusted to our needs. If the atmosphere had been much thinner, some of the meteors which are now burned in the outer atmosphere by the millions every day would strike all parts of the earth. They travel from six to forty miles a second and would set fire to every burnable object. If they traveled as slowly as a bullet, they would all hit the earth and the consequences would be dire. As for man, the impact of a tiny meteor traveling ninety times as fast as a bullet would tear him in pieces by the heat of its passage. The atmosphere is just thick enough to let in the actinic rays needed for vegetation and to kill bacteria, produce vitamins, and not harm man unless he exposes himself too long. In spite of all the gaseous emanations from the earth of all the ages, most of them poisonous, the atmosphere remains practically uncontaminated and unchanging in its balanced relationship necessary to man's very existence.

The great balance wheel is that vast mass of water, the ocean, from which have come life, food, rain, temperate climate, plants, animals, and ultimately man himself. Let him who comprehends this stand in awe before its majesty and gratefully acknowledge his obligations.

## III

### *The Gases We Breathe*

ET us take oxygen as an illustration of almost infinite adjustment. The atmosphere of the earth is composed of oxygen, nitrogen, argon, neon, xenon, and krypton. It contains water vapor and 3/100 of one per cent, or about three parts in 10,000 of carbon dioxide. The rare gases manifest themselves conspicuously in affording the reds, blues and greens of the advertising signs, and argon, of which 9/10 of one per cent is present in the atmosphere, gives us the superbly brilliant electric lights which are advancing civilization wherever used. Nitrogen exists to approximately 78 per cent of the atmosphere, and oxygen is commonly placed at 21 per cent. The atmosphere as a whole presses upon the earth at approximately fifteen pounds on each square inch of surface at sea level. The oxygen which exists in the atmosphere is a part of this pressure, being about three pounds per square inch. All the rest of the oxygen is locked up in the form of compounds in the crust of the earth and makes up 8/10 of all the waters in the world. Oxygen is the breath of life for all land animals and is for this purpose utterly unobtainable except from the atmosphere.

24

The question arises how this extremely active chemical element escaped combination and was left in the atmosphere in the almost exact proportion necessary for practically all living things. If, for instance, instead of 21 per cent oxygen were 50 per cent or more of the atmosphere, all combustible substances in the world would become inflammable to such an extent that the first stroke of lightning to hit a tree would ignite the forest, which would almost explode. If it were reduced to 10 per cent or less, life might through the ages have adjusted itself to it, but few of the elements of civilization now so familiar to man, such as fire, would be available. If free oxygen, this one part in many millions of the earth's substance, should be absorbed, all animal life would cease.

The curious relationship between oxygen and carbon dioxide in respect to the life of animals and the entire vegetable world has been brought to the attention of all thinking people, but the importance of carbon dioxide is still not generally comprehended. It may be said in passing that carbon dioxide is the familiar gas used in charging soda water. It is a stubborn, heavy gas that fortunately clings close to the earth. Its separation into oxygen and carbon is accomplished only with great difficulty. When you light a fire, the wood, being chiefly composed of oxygen, carbon, and hydrogen, decomposes under the influence of heat, the carbon combines with the oxygen with great vigor and the result is carbon dioxide. The hydrogen released combines with equal vigor with the oxygen and we get water vapor. The smoke is mostly uncombined carbon. When a man breathes, he draws in oxygen, which is taken up by the blood and distributed through his body. This oxygen burns his food in every cell very slowly at a comparatively low temperature, but the result is carbon dioxide and water vapor, so when a man is said to sigh like a furnace, there is a touch of reality about it. The carbon dioxide escapes into his lungs and is not breathable except in small quantities. It sets his lungs in action and he takes his next breath throwing into the atmosphere carbon dioxide. All animal life is thus absorbing oxygen and throwing off carbon dioxide. Oxygen is further essential to life because of its action upon other elements in the blood as well as elsewhere in the body, without which life processes would cease.

On the other hand, as is well known, all vegetable life is dependent upon the almost infinitesimal quantity of carbon dioxide in the atmosphere which, so to speak, it breathes. To express this complicated photosynthetic chemical reaction in the simplest possible way, the leaves of the trees are lungs and they have the power when in the sunlight to separate this obstinate carbon dioxide into carbon and oxygen. In other words, the oxygen is given off and the carbon retained and combined with the hydrogen of the water brought up by the plant from its roots. By magical chemistry, out of these elements nature makes sugar, cellulose and numerous other chemicals, fruits and flowers. The plant feeds itself and produces enough more to feed every animal on earth. At the same time, the plant releases the oxygen we breathe and without which life would end in five minutes. Let us, then, pay our humble respects to the plant. So all the plants, the forests, the grasses, every bit of moss, and all else of vegetable life, build their structure principally out of carbon and water. Animals give off carbon dioxide and plants give off oxygen. If this interchange did not take place, either the animal or the vegetable life would ultimately use up practically all of the oxygen or all of the carbon dioxide, and the balance, being completely upset, one would wilt or die and the other would quickly follow. It has recently been discovered that carbon dioxide in small quantities is also essential to most animal life, just as plants use some oxygen.

Hydrogen must be included, although we do not breathe it. Without hydrogen water would not exist, and the water content of animal and vegetable matter is surprisingly great and absolutely essential. Oxygen, hydrogen, carbon dioxide, and carbon, singly and in their various relations to each other, are the principal biological elements. They are the very basis on which life rests. There is, however, not one chance in millions that they should all be at one time on one planet in the proper proportions for life. Science has no explanations to offer for the facts, and to say it is accidental is to defy mathematics.

# IV

## *Nitrogen, a Double Adjustment*

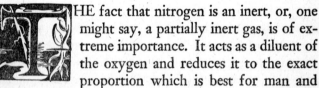HE fact that nitrogen is an inert, or, one might say, a partially inert gas, is of extreme importance. It acts as a diluent of the oxygen and reduces it to the exact proportion which is best for man and animals. As illustrated in the case of oxygen, we have neither too much nor too little nitrogen. It might be said that man has adapted himself to the 21 per cent of oxygen in the air and this is true, but the fact that this quantity is the exact amount that is best for him in other essential ways adds further interest. So, curiously, we find the definite proportion of oxygen due to two factors. First, it was not absorbed completely, thus becoming a part of the crust of the earth or of the ocean, and, further, the quantity left free is the exact quantity which the total amount of nitrogen would properly dilute. Had nitrogen been present in much more or less volume, man as we know him could not have developed. Here is a remarkable double adjustment. Nitrogen, as an inert gas, is apparently useless, and this is chemically true of the condition in which it is found in the atmosphere. Of course, it is 78 per cent of every breeze that blows. It is a part of the protecting atmosphere without which many hazardous things

would happen. But in neither sense is nitrogen now as vitally essential to man and vegetation as is oxygen.

But there is a series of chemicals of which nitrogen forms a part and which may be spoken of in a general sense as combined nitrogen—nitrogen which can be taken up by plants, nitrogen which forms the nitrogenous element in our foods without which man would starve. There are but two ways in which soluble nitrogen can get into the soil as a fertilizer, and without nitrogen in some form not a food plant could grow. One way in which nitrogen can get into the soil is through the activities of certain bacteria which inhabit the roots of leguminous plants, such as clover, peas, beans, and many others. These bacteria take atmospheric nitrogen and turn it into combined nitrogen, and when the plant dies some of this combined nitrogen is left in the soil. Another way in which nitrogen gets into the soil is through thunderstorms. Whenever a flash of lightning rushes through the atmosphere, it combines a very small quantity of the oxygen with the nitrogen and the rain brings it to the earth as combined nitrogen. These two methods have been inadequate and that is the reason that long-cultivated fields have lost their nitrogen. This is the reason why the farmer rotates his crops. Malthus prophesied long ago that, with the increasing population of the earth and the using of the land for continuous crops, in time the fertilizing elements would be exhausted. Had his calculation as to increasing population been correct, some time early in the present century the scarcity point would have been reached. This illustrates the importance of the tenuous residue of nitrogen left in the atmosphere, so very little in relation to the mass of the whole earth. Without nitrogen, man and most animals would die.

Curiously, at the point where starvation was clearly understood as a possibility of the future, and that is within the last forty years, processes have been found by which combined nitrogen can be produced from the atmosphere, and more recently it has been demonstrated that it can be produced in prodigious quantities. This fear of world starvation has been removed. It is interesting to note that one of the attempts to produce combined nitrogen was the imitation under suitable conditions of nature in the production of artificial electrical storms. Nearly 300,000 horse-power are said to have been utilized in creating electrical arcs in the atmosphere and, sure enough, as had been demonstrated long before, a residue of combined nitrogen was produced. But now the ingenuity of man has gone farther, and after ten thousand years of historical existence, has developed the methods by which he transforms an inert gas into a fertilizer. This enables him to produce a necessary element in food without which man would starve. What a coincidence that man has acquired at this exact time in the earth's history the ability to ward off universal food shortage. The ethical results of being forced to reduce the population of the earth in order that some might survive are too terrible to contemplate. This tragedy has been averted at the exact moment when it could have been anticipated.

# V

## *What Is Life?*

IFE is immortal. It has outlived eons and geologic ages. Continents have arisen and have been submerged. The ancient oceans and the shallow seas teamed with life. It sounds the depths; it permeates the crest of the breaking wave and the sands of every shore. It has advanced with every retreat of every ice age; vigorous and undefeated, it has resisted each frigid advance. Mountains have arisen from the wrinkled earth, the surface has cracked and trembled with the quake. The record of millions of years of erosion that erased the mountains' vast heights is shown, strata on strata. The continents have been washed into the sea. The silt of the ancient lands, like a shroud, veils the bottom of every ocean, but life has survived.

Life uses the atoms of the earth, and, following the laws of the universe, creates new wonders but leaves behind as it advances every particle it has touched. The "White Cliffs of Dover," made up of chalk, lime and flint, tell the story of mollusk and diatom and the myriad creatures of the sea through the ages. The living forests, coal, oil and gas, evidence the activities of the ancient world in which life caught the energy of the sun, which man releases as fire. This legacy surpasses in value all other wealth, for it has lifted man above the animal. Out of the furnace of the beginnings of the earth's crust, where all matter was reduced to cinders and ashes, life has used the energy of the sun, torn asunder the combined atoms of water and the sluggish carbon from its oxygen in carbon dioxide and stored throughout the earth and over its surface the only sources of fire. From fire came the home and all the implements of civilization, all this because life has both caught and held the forces released by the sun.

Life has conquered the varied conditions of water, land and air, and moves on as plant and animal. From amœba, up to fish, insect, mammal, and birds of the air, or down to germ, microbe, and bacteria, as well as the numberless plants, whether as cell, shark, spider, dinosaur, man, or vegetation, life masters the elements and compels them to dissolve their combinations and recombine in new relations. Life produces creations of varied designs in the image of its predecessors and gives them the power to repeat themselves for untold generations. Life is so prolific in its reproduction that it makes its own sustenance and feeds upon its own surplus, yet controls all living things so that none of its creatures shall overrun the world. The locusts, if uncontrolled, would in a few years eat every green thing, and all animal life above water would cease to exist.

Life is a sculptor and shapes all living things; an artist that designs every leaf of every tree, that colors the flowers, the apple, the forest, and the plumage of the bird of paradise. Life is a musician and has taught each bird to sing its love songs, the insects to call each other in the music of their multitudinous sounds. These sounds, from the springtime cheepings of the frog and the motherly cluck of the hen to the triumphant roar of the lion and the trumpeting of the elephant, cover the whole gamut of emotion, surpassed only by the astounding flexibility of the human voice.

Life has given to man alone mastery over combined sound vibrations and has furnished the material for their production. The reed, the horn and the harp, as well as the horsehair and rosin on the violin bow drawn across animal fiber, the resonance of the wood winds of the orchestra and the "unctuous" grunt of the double bass and the thump of leather on leather of the drum owe a debt to life.

Life is an engineer, for it has designed the legs of the grasshopper and the flea, the co-ordinated muscles, levers and joints, the tireless beating heart, the system of electric nerves of every animal, and the complete system of circulation of every living thing. It designs the dandelion and then adorns its seeds in tassels, which are thus carried on every breeze. Life shapes the flowers and compels the insects to bear the pollen from stamen to pistil.

Life is a chemist that gives taste to our fruits and spices and perfume to the rose. Life synthesizes new substances which Nature has not yet provided to balance its processes and to destroy invading life. Life gives cold light to the firefly to aid his nocturnal love-making. Life's chemistry is sublime, for not only does it set the rays of the sun to work to change water and carbonic acid into wood and sugar, but, in doing so, releases oxygen that animals may have the breath of life.

Life is a historian, for it has written its history page by page, through the ages, leaving its record in the rocks, an autobiography which only awaits correct interpretation. Life gives its creatures the joy of living. The lamb frisks and gambols, not knowing why. Life colors and gives sparkle to the eyes of a child, tints his cheeks and brings laughter to his lips. Matter never smiles.

Life protects its creations by the abundance of food in the egg and prepares many of its infants for active life after birth, or by unconscious motherhood stores food in preparation for her young. Life produces life —giving milk to meet immediate needs, foreseeing this necessity and preparing for events to come. Life has brought into the world mother love, and for man, the shelter of the home, the family, and the love of country for which he will fight and die. Life protects itself by a cautious use of colors to aid or to conceal its creatures; it gives legs for speed, protective armament, horns, jaws and claws; in hearing, sight and smell, provides for offense and defense, and wings designed for flight. Life provides a fearsome mask for some of its most innocent insects and thus protects them from attack.

Matter has never done more than its laws decree. The atoms and molecules obey the dictates of chemical affinity, the force of gravity, the influences of temperature and electric impulses. Matter has no initiative, but life brings into being marvelous new designs and structures. Without life, the surface of the earth would be a vast tractless desert and a waste of useless water. Without life, matter is inert and when life leaves it, it is again merely matter, but it still has the power to continue the life of other creatures and so perpetuates life in other living things. Whence it came or where it goes, science answers not.

What life is no man has yet fathomed; it has no weight or dimensions. Life has force, for a growing root will crack a rock. Life builds a mighty tree and holds it against gravity for a thousand years or more. It lifts tons of water from the earth each day and builds the leaves and fruits. The oldest living thing is a tree, and this covers a span of five thousand years—a moment in eternity. So individual life is fleeting. Life accounts for every motion of every living thing, and almost all this energy comes through the rays of the sun.

Life cannot survive in matter which is, in very narrow limits, too hot or too cold, because both destroy the conditions of matter on which it depends. Life manifested itself on this earth only when the conditions were suitable to it, and will cease its activities when any marked change takes place. But present conditions have existed for at least three hundred million years. Nature did not create life; fire-blistered rocks and a saltless sea did not meet the necessary requirements. Did Life brood over this earth and "other earths," awaiting its opportunity to glorify Cosmos with understanding? Gravity is a property of matter; electricity we now believe to be matter itself; the rays of the sun and stars can be deflected by gravity and seem to be akin to it. Man is learning the dimensions of the atom and is measuring its locked-up power, but life is illusive, like space. WHY?

Life is undeviating in the execution of its effort to animate matter; it knows no joy or tragedy and makes no distinctions; yet life is fundamental and is the only means by which matter can attain understanding. Life is the only source of consciousness and it alone makes possible knowledge of the works of God which we, still half blind, yet know to be good. Life is an instrumentality serving the purposes of the Supreme Intelligence. *LIFE IS IMMORTAL.*

# VI

## *How Life Began*

HERE is a point in the mystery of life's beginnings where the scientist must now stop for lack of evidence. There is an abundance of circumstantial evidence and it can be well and scientifically stated. The origin of life itself is so marvelous, and the subsequent results so divergent, and so far beyond comprehension, that even the most learned biologist is astounded. As a scientist he cannot believe in miracles, but as an intelligent human being he sees as a result of his study and the work of all others that following emergence from the sub-microscopic, near molecular twilight zone of life, most living things now develop from a single microscopic cell. This cell seems to have been endowed with the unbelievable power to multiply and fit itself into the myriad forms of life, adapted to exist in every nook and cranny of the earth's surface. Science acknowledges that facts cannot be otherwise. Some believe that it is an accident of chemicals, water and time. Others see order in each vast phalanx of divergent life as it presses forward from the same source to its destiny, whether it is to become a mollusk or a man, never again to bridge the gap. Let us approach the subject with a sense of reverence, unbound by the strict limitations imposed by religious creeds or scientific certainty as to the cause and source of life, and picture to ourselves the admitted facts. Thus we can judge with the matter fully before us. We may thus learn whether you and I are merely a fortuitous aggregation of matter born of chemicals, water and time, or not.

Behold the only thing of consequence, more important than the earth itself, or the universe. More important than all else, unless there is an intelligent Creator who caused it to exist—an almost invisible drop of protoplasm, transparent, jelly-like, capable of motion, drawing energy from the sun. It is already capable of using the light of the sun to break up the carbon dioxide in the air, forcing the atoms apart, seizing the hydrogen from the water and producing carbohydrates, thus making its own food out of one of the world's most stubborn chemical compounds.

This single cell, this transparent mistlike droplet, holds within itself the germ of all life, and has the power to distribute this life to every living thing, great and small, and fits that creature to its environment wherever life can exist, from the bottom of the ocean to the sky. Time and environment have molded the form of every living thing to meet this infinite variety of conditions, and as these living things developed their individuality, they sacrificed some of their flexibility to change and became specialized and fixed, losing the power to go back but gaining in better adjustment to the conditions as they existed for them.

The powers of this droplet of protoplasm and its contents were and are greater than the vegetation that clothes the earth in green, greater than all the animals that breathe the breath of life, for all life came from it and without it no living thing would have been or could be.

Science agrees to all that step by step has been set forth above, but hesitates to take a final one and add: Man has by this path strutted this earth as a child of the universal source of life, masterful among animals, a material structure infinitely complex, possessing a brain purposely prepared for and destined to receive a spark of the Supreme Intelligence, which we call a soul.

We must begin with the whole earth a desert and only those substances left when the earth cooled down. The land had risen from the oceans, and untold erosion had torn apart the rocks and built up vast secondary rocks, silt and sediment. Only inorganic substances existed in such combinations as basalt, granite, and those other igneous and metamorphic rocks and the silt which preceded the residues of animal existence. The residues such as limestone, coral, chalk, and flint did not exist. We have few substances to deal with. We have water and probably a very constant temperature. The mystery of the advent of life upon the earth may or may not have been solved by its spontaneous occurrence. It has been suggested by some that life arrived from some planet as a germ which escaped unharmed and after an eternity in space settled upon the earth. Such a germ could hardly survive the absolute zero temperature of space, and if it did, the intense short-wave radiation would kill it. Here, if it survived, it must have found the right place, the ocean probably, where an amazing combination of circumstances brought about its re-birth and the beginning of life here. Besides, this puts the question back one step, for we can ask how did life originate on any planet. It has been generally held that neither mere environment, no matter how favorable to life, nor any combination of chemical and physical conditions which could be brought about by chance, can bring life into existence. Disregarding this question of the origin of life, which is, of course, a scientific mystery, it has been suggested that a little speck of matter, a giant molecule, but still so small that no regular microscope could even glimpse it, added atoms, upset its cohesive balance, divided, and the separate parts repeated the cycle, and thus took on the aspects of life; but no one yet claims it took on life itself.

An amœba is a microscopic, highly developed living creature composed of untold millions of atoms in orderly arrangement. Amœbas are single-celled creatures, perhaps a hundredth of an inch in diameter, found in all waters of the world. An amœba feels hunger and deliberately and with purpose pursues its food. How big must an animal be before we acknowledge it has desires and determination? Size is nothing to the Infinite, for the atom is as perfect as the solar system. Using an amœba as an illustration, but with no suggestion that this living creature is the original single-celled source of life, some protoplasmic living creature, an original source of life, having duplicated its internal structure, divided and formed two. The two divided and formed four, and so on infinitely, as cells do today in every living creature. Each cell contains within itself in the early division the power to produce a complete individual. The cells themselves, except for accident or insurmountable changes of condition, are immortal. They form the simple cells of all creatures, animal or vegetable of today, and thus may be exact replicas of their progenitors. We as human beings are well-ordered republics of billions on billions of similar cells, each cell a citizen intelligently doing its full quota of devoted service. Quite a change from an inanimate molecule.

But one can point out something that happened far back in the beginning of life on earth that is of prodigious importance. One cell developed the astounding power to use sunlight to break up a chemical compound and make its own food and enough for its brother cells. Other children of some original cell must have lived upon food produced by the first cell and become animal, while the first cell became vegetable, whose descendants, the plants, feed all living things today. Can we believe that the fact that one cell became animal and another a vegetable was brought about by chance? It is here in this division that the wonderful balance between vegetation and animal life was established. Reverting back to the story of carbon dioxide, we find that this division was absolutely basic as one of the essentials of life itself.

If all life were animal, it would by now have used up all the oxygen; or if all life were vegetable, it would have exhausted all the carbon dioxide. In either case, both would be dead.

As stated before, it is suggested that there was in the very early history of the earth no free oxygen in the air, all oxygen being locked up in the crust of the earth, in water and carbon dioxide. If this were the case, all the oxygen we now have has come from vegetation. This has been pretty well proved to be possible, as plants use up carbon dioxide and release the oxygen; but if all this be true, animals which must have oxygen to live, must have come into existence long after plants in the sea and on land had developed. Were there two advents of life? We will leave this for the future to decide.

How amazingly, in both animal and vegetable life, from the advent of the first protoplasmic beings, male and female developed so that every species by repeated recombination would be continued with its general characteristics preserved.

It is beyond our present scope to consider in detail the physico-chemical compulsions and sequences which actuate differentiation. For our purpose is to make the matter understandable to those without special scientific training. The matter may be stated about as follows:

Apparently, the groups of cells survived more frequently when in close relationship, and so they began to combine in twos and fours and hundreds and thousands, and ultimately millions. Each cell was now called upon to perform an allotted task. Gradually, as these different tasks were assigned, new activities for the group became possible. In animals the cilia, little hairlike structures, or the pseudopods, false feet, aided in gathering food which other cells were active in digesting. Some parts were composed of many cells. One set made a thick protective covering, as the bark of a tree. Others were busy transporting food from one place to another in the living creature. Finally, we find them busily forming wood in trunks or bones or shells to support their combined growing bulk. Some shells were placed outside, like those of a clam. These mollusks are "shut-ins." Some bones were built inside. Man needs "backbone." All things that live start from a simple cell, and this cell compels all its descendants to perform the services and follow without deviation the design of the creature the original cell was to duplicate, whether it is a turtle or a rabbit.

The question may arise whether or not cells are intelligent. Whether we believe that nature has endowed cells either with instinct, whatever that is, or reasoning power, we must admit that cells are forced to change their shape and entire nature to meet the requirements of the being of which they are a part. Every cell that is produced in any living creature must adapt itself to be part of the flesh, to sacrifice itself as a part of the skin, which will soon be worn off. It must deposit the enamel of teeth, produce the transparent liquid in an eye, or become a nose, or an ear. Each cell must then adapt itself in shape and every other characteristic necessary to fulfill its function. It is hard to think of a cell as right-handed or left-handed, but one becomes part of a right ear, the other becomes part of the left ear. Some crystals that are chemically identical turn the rays of light to the left, others to the right. There seems to be such a tendency in the cells. In the exact place where they belong, they become a part of the right ear or the left ear, and your two ears are opposite each other on your head, and not as in the case of a cricket on your elbows. Their curves are opposite, and when complete, they are so much alike you cannot tell them apart. Hundreds of thousands of cells seem impelled to do the right thing at the right time in the right place, and verily they are obedient. Life pushes forward, building, repairing, extending, and creating the new and the better with an irresistible energy not found in inanimate things. Is this intelligence? is it instinct? or does it just happen? You can answer this yourself.

But you may now say that nothing in this chapter has explained how life began, that is, how it came to this earth. The writer does not know, but he believes it came as an expression of Divine power, and it is not material.

# VII

## *Origin of Man*

HERE are several ways of looking at the origin of man. An examination of these ways will be disturbing to many who have fixed opinions. One view is that man came up through a process of evolution from the original spark of life. This is the basis on which the whole concept of evolution rests. Another is that God in His wisdom put life upon the earth and made man as he is or was, perfect. Another view is that the Divine Providence is not static, but has produced life in all its phases by a series of creations. Still another is that life which ultimately developed into man was the happy result of a chance mixture of chemicals, including water. It may be asserted that, assuming a Creator, He sought to create from the original elements of the earth something that should have life and ultimately reach a development of brain in which intelligence could be placed. It may be assumed that He proposed to give that intelligence mastery and domination over all other living things and over many that are inanimate. Whichever of these varied propositions you may choose, it is clear that man could not have had an existence as man since life began, but was developed later. In any event, he did not appear as man until the total inadequacy of every other form of life to develop a mechanism as infinitely complex as the human brain was proved. Assuming that man had his beginnings in the original advent of life, he has had an existence of possibly 400 million years or much more. Assuming the second theory, he may have come into existence subsequently or at any time as a result of the divine command. If we accept the third proposition, we cannot date his first existence as man at any time less than many million years ago. Man as such has been traced back with sufficient evidence to satisfy scientists for about one million years, but this is already an established minimum. Before that, his evolution, from whatever animal he may have developed, goes back to an antiquity beyond all human calculation.

In the American Museum of Natural History in New York there is a fossil three-toed horse, a little animal which could undoubtedly run with much speed. He was unquestionably a horse, but his evolution into the present splendid animal which runs on what we call a hoof developed from one toe, took millions of years. Using this as a guide-post, then, measure the time that man has taken to develop hand, eye, and brain and thus become an inconsequential animal and thereafter rise to his present status. Now, let us again measure the vicissitudes through which this defenseless little creature has passed, agile indeed, but subject to danger from every carnivorous creature and every poisonous reptile and every disease producing organism. He had to care for his young through a long period of infant helplessness. The children of man are born helpless and they come in sequence, so that several helpless babies may become dependent upon constant nurture and protection at one time. This multiplies the wonder of man's survival through the ages. He lived through such changes as the Ice Age and every other vicissitude of unprotected life. Of course, this is true of all other animals. It is one of the marvels of God's providence that these creatures were able to meet the conditions. On the other hand, untold numbers of the species which have been born have ceased to exist. Bones of dinosaurs are but one evidence by which geologists prove that weird creatures of the past were unsuccessful and have passed into oblivion. And so with millions of insects, fish, birds, and many more species of infinitesimal creatures. The passenger pigeon at one time probably outnumbered man, but the last one died within our memory and his magnificent race is as dead as the great auk and the dodo.

Archæologists showing the development of man indicate the brain capacity of his skull as the key to his progress. Races of men have been and are now being superseded by others of which the white race seems to be at the moment on top. Will time bring into being a superman who will breed true and crowd us off the earth? In an infant's skull the bones are separated by a cartilage which allows for further growth of its

brain, and this may continue into youth if such capacity is needed; but we do become "hard-headed" a
bit early and it behooves us not to close our minds to
truth too soon.

# VIII

## Animal Instincts

HE evolution of man is physically well advanced and there seems no chance for the growth of new bodily structure. There should, however, be better health, and because of diet and the wonders of medicine and surgery, a more complete physical development. On the average, therefore, there should be better brains. At least, there is a better opportunity for good mentality to express itself, and thus advance man's material, ethical, and spiritual condition, both as an individual and as a race. Civilization and the acceptance of ethical standards move forward and backward, but there is always a gain, and man's development has been very notable; but he has far to go. Fortunately, there seems to be no limit to possible new developments in the human brain with time, real time, as the controlling factor.

Birds have the homing instinct. The robin that nested at your door goes south in the fall, but comes back to his old nest the next spring. In September, flocks of most of our birds fly south, often over a thousand miles of open ocean, but they do not lose their way. The homing pigeon, confused by new sounds on a long journey in a closed box, circles for a moment and then heads almost unerringly for home. The bee finds its hive while the wind waving the grasses and trees blots out every visible guide to its whereabouts. This homing sense is slightly developed in man, but he supplements his meager equipment with instruments of navigation. We need this instinct and our brain provides the answer. The tiny insects must have microscopic eyes, how perfect we do not know, and the hawks, the eagle and the condor must have telescopic vision. Here again man surpasses them with his mechanical instruments. With his telescope he can see a nebula so faint that it requires two million times his vision, and with the electron miscroscope he can see hitherto invisible bacteria, and, so to speak, the little bugs that bite them.

If you let old Dobbin alone he will keep to the road in the blackest night. He can see, dimly perhaps, but he notes the difference in temperature of the road and the sides with eyes that are slightly affected by the infra-red rays of the road. The owl can see the nice warm mouse as he runs in the cooler grass in the blackest night. We turn night into day by creating radiation in that short octave we call light.

The lens of your eye throws an image on the retina, and the muscles automatically adjust the lens to a perfect focus. The retina is composed of nine separate layers, all of which together are no thicker than thin paper. The inmost layer is made up of rods and cones, which are said to number thirty million rods and three million cones. These are all arranged in perfect relation to each other and to the lens, but, strangely enough, they turn their backs upon the lens and look inward, not outward. If you could look out through the lens you would see your enemy upside down and right side left. A bit confusing if you tried to defend yourself. So by some means nature knew what would happen, and before the eye could really see, made the correction, developing through the millions of nerve filaments leading to the brain a complete readjustment; then raised our octave of perception from heat to light, thus making the eye sensitive to color. We are thus seeing a colored picture of the world right side up, a good optical provision. The lens of our eye varies in density so that all rays are brought into focus. Man finds this unattainable in any homogeneous substance, such as glass. All the marvelous adjustments of lens, rods, cones, nerves, and all else must have occurred simultaneously, for before each of them was complete, sight was impossible. How could one necessary factor know and adjust itself to each of the requirements of the others?

The ordinary scallop whose muscle we eat has several dozen beautiful eyes very like ours, which sparkle because each eye has unnumbered little reflectors which are said to enable it to see things right side up. These reflectors are not found in the human eye. Were these reflectors developed because of the absence of superior brain power in the scallop? As the number of eyes in animals ranges from two to thousands, and all are different, Nature would have had a big job in developing the science of optics unless somewhere along the line there was a little help from Intelligence.

The honey bee is not attracted by the gaudy flowers as we see them, but sees by the ultra-violet light, which may make them even more beautiful to bees. From the rays of slower vibrations to the photographic plate and beyond are realms of beauty, joy, and inspiration which we are just beginning to appreciate and control. Let us hope that we can some day enjoy this wider realm of light by means of inventive genius. We can already detect the heat vibration of a distant star and measure its energy.

The honey-bee workers make chambers of different sizes in the comb used for breeding. Small chambers are constructed for the workers, larger ones for the drones, and special chambers for the prospective queens. The queen bee lays unfertilized eggs in the cells designed for males, but lays fertilized eggs in the proper chambers for the female workers and the possible queens. The workers, who are the modified females, having long since anticipated the coming of the new generation, are also prepared to furnish food for the young bees by chewing and predigesting honey and pollen. They discontinue the process of chewing, including the predigesting, at a certain stage of the development of the males and females, and feed only honey and pollen. The females so treated become the workers.

For the females in the queen chambers the diet of chewed and predigested food is continued. These specially treated females develop into queen bees, which alone produce fertile eggs. This process of reproduction involves special chambers, special eggs, and the marvelous effect of a change of diet. This means anticipation, discretion, and the application of a discovery of the effect of diet. These changes apply particularly to a community life and seem necessary to its existence. The knowledge and skills required must have been evolved after the beginnings of this community life, and are not necessarily inherent in the structure or the survival of the honey bee as such. The bee, therefore, seems to have outstripped man in knowledge of the effects of diet under certain conditions.

The dog with an inquiring nose can sense the animal that has passed. No instrument of human invention has added to our inferior sense of smell, and we hardly know where to begin to investigate its extension. Yet even our sense of smell is so highly developed that it can detect ultra-microscopic particles. How do we know that we all get the same reaction from any single odor? The fact is that we do not. Taste also gives a very different sensation to each of us. How strange that these differences in perception are hereditary.

All animals hear sounds, many of which are outside our range of vibration, with an acuteness that far surpasses our limited sense of hearing. Man by his devices can now hear a fly walking miles away as though he were on his eardrums, and with like instruments record the impact of a cosmic ray.

A part of the human ear is a series of some four

thousand minute but complex arches graduated with exquisite regularity in size and shape. These may be said to resemble a musical instrument, and they seem adjusted to catch, and transmit in some manner to the brain, every cadence of sound or noise, from the thunderclap to the whisper of the pines and the exquisite blending of the tones and harmonies of every instrument in the orchestra. If in forming the ear the cells were impelled to evolve strict efficiency only that man might survive, why did they not extend the range and develop a superacuteness? Perhaps the power behind these cells' activities anticipated man's coming need of intellectual enjoyment, or did they by accident build better than they knew?

One of the water spiders fashions a balloon-shaped nest of cobweb filaments and attaches it to some object under water. Then she ingeniously entangles an air bubble in the hairs of her under body, carries it into the water, and releases it under the nest. This performance is repeated until the nest is inflated, when she proceeds to bring forth and raise her young safe from attack by air. Here we have a synthesis of the web, engineering, construction, and aeronautics. Chance perhaps, but that still leaves the spider unexplained.

The young salmon spends years at sea, then comes back to his own river, and, what is more, he travels up the side of the river into which flows the tributary in which he was born. The laws of the States on one side of the dividing stream may be strict and the other side not, but these laws affect only the fish which may be said to belong to each side. What brings them back so definitely? If a salmon going up a river is transferred to another tributary he will at once realize he is not in the right tributary and will fight his way down to the main stream and then turn up against the current to finish his destiny. There is, however, a much more difficult problem in the exact reverse to solve in the case of the eel. These amazing creatures migrate at maturity from all the ponds and rivers everywhere—those from Europe across thousands of miles of ocean—all go to the abysmal deeps south of Bermuda. There they breed and die. The little ones, with no apparent means of knowing anything except that they are in a wilderness of water, start back and find their way to the shore from which their parents came and thence to every river, lake and little pond, so that each body of water is always populated with eels. They have braved the mighty currents, storms, and tides, and have conquered the beating waves on every shore. They can now grow and when they are mature, they will, by some mysterious law, go back through it all to complete the cycle. Where does the directing impulse originate? No American eel has ever been caught in European waters and no European eel has ever been caught in American waters. Nature has also delayed the maturity of the European eel by a year or more to make up for its much greater journey. Do atoms and molecules when combined in an eel have a sense of direction and will power to exercise it?

Animals seem to have telepathy. Who has not

watched with admiration the sandpiper flying and wheeling till every white breast shows in the sunlight at the same instant?

A female moth placed in your attic by the open window will send out some subtle signal. Over an unbelievable area, the male moths of the same species will catch the message and respond in spite of your attempts to produce laboratory odors to disconcert them. Has the little creature a broadcasting station, and has the male moth a mental radio set besides his antennae? Does she shake the ether and does he catch the vibration? The katydid rubs its legs or wings together, and on a still night can be heard half a mile away. It shakes six hundred tons of air and calls its mate. Miss Moth, working in a different realm of physics and, in apparent silence, calls quite as effectively. Before the radio was discovered, scientists decided it was odor that attracted the male moth. It is a miracle either way, because the odor would have to travel in all directions, with or without the wind. The male moth would have to be able to detect a molecule and sense the direction from whence it came. By a vast mechanism, we are developing the same ability to communicate, and the day will come when a young man may call his loved one from a distance and without mechanical medium and she will answer. No lock or bars will stop them. Our telephone and radio are instrumental wonders and give us the means of almost instant communication, but we are tied to a wire and a place. The moth is still ahead of us, and we can only envy her until our brain evolves an individual radio. Then, in a sense, we will have telepathy.

Vegetation makes subtle use of involuntary agents to carry on its existence—insects to carry pollen from flower to flower and the winds and everything that flies or walks to distribute seed. At last, vegetation has trapped masterful man. He has improved nature, and she generously rewards him. But he has multiplied so prodigiously that he is now chained to the plow. He must sow, reap, and store; breed and cross-breed; prune and graft. Should he neglect these chores starvation would be his lot, civilization would crumble, and earth return to her pristine state.

Birds taken from their nests when they were young will, when mature, build nests in the pattern of their species. Hereditary habits have their origin deep in the mists of antiquity. Are these distinctive acts the result of chance or of an intelligent provision? This is enough to show the power of hereditary habit, which we call instinct. Among all the living creatures that have roamed the earth none has a record of reasoning power which may compare with that of man. There is survival because of adjustment and extinction because adjustment has gone too far. But only man has developed a knowledge of numbers. If an insect could know how many legs it has, it still could not tell the total number of legs of two of its kind. This requires reasoning power.

Many animals are like a lobster, which, having lost a claw, will by some restimulation of the cells and the reactivation of the genes discover that a part of the body is missing and restore it. When the work is complete, the cells stop work, for in some way they know it is quitting time. A fresh-water polyp divided into halves can reform itself out of one of these halves. Cut off an angle worm's head and he will soon create a new one. We can stimulate healing, but when will our surgeons, if ever, know how to stimulate the cells to produce a new arm, flesh, bones, nails, and activating nerves? An extraordinary fact throws some light on this mystery of re-creation. If cells in the early stages of development are separated, each has the ability to create a complete animal. Therefore, if the original cell divides into two and they are separated, two individuals will be developed. This may account for identical twins, but it means much more—each cell at first is in detail potentially a complete individual. There can be no doubt, then, that you are you in every cell and fiber. The marvelous manner in which a single cell may develop into an individual being is simply and truly stated in Psalm 139:14-16:

"I will praise thee; for I am fearfully and wonderfully made; marvelous are thy works; and that my soul knoweth right well.

My substance was not hid from thee, when I was made in secret, and curiously wrought in the lowest parts of the earth.

Thine eyes did see my substance, yet being unperfect; and in thy book all my members were written, which in continuance were fashioned, when as yet there was none of them."

Pages could be devoted to the wonders of sense quite beyond our present knowledge, but these illustrations are quite enough to show we have much to learn. Until man develops new senses or can equal the animals by mechanisms in each of their special abilities, he has a long vista of evolution ahead of him. Each animal ability which we do not possess is a challenge to our genius, and until we find the answer, we are not fully informed. We cannot yet understand instinct or generalize safely on incomplete knowledge. Until we possess every sense gained by living things, we will be unable to realize the real interrelationship of the laws of nature and discuss the infinite with more than a partial understanding. The misuse of our new powers is the crude expression of undeveloped minds. The spiritual development of man is just beginning. The Divine spark is now slowly gaining control of his material brain. His errors, even carried to self-destruction, are nothing but the tragedies of childhood. Our time measured by past eternity and the eternity to come is as the tick of a clock, but the spirit within us belongs to both.

When we think of space ever extending, of time with no beginning and no end, of the energy controlled and held captive in the atom, of the limitless cosmos with unnumbered universes and myriad of stars; of the vibrations we call light, heat, electricity, and magnetism; of the persistent energy of the stars, of gravity and the universal reign of law, we understand how little we really know. How much man must advance before he fully realizes the existence of a Supreme Intelligence and strives to live up to the highest code he is capable of understanding without attempting to analyze God's motives or describe His attributes.

# IX

## *The Development of Mind*

OW utterly strange it is that in the innumerable varieties of animal life, living and extinct, there is but little evidence of mentality other than instinct until we come to man himself. No animal has left a record of its ability to square a stone or to count ten or understand the meaning of ten.

In the mêlée of creation many creatures have come to exhibit a high degree of certain forms of instinct, intelligence, or what not. The wasp catches the grasshopper, digs a hole in the earth, stings the grasshopper in exactly the right place so that he becomes unconscious but lives as a form of preserved meat. The wasp lays her eggs exactly in the right place, perhaps not knowing that when they hatch, her children can eat without killing the insect on which they feed, which would be fatal to them. The wasp must have done all this right the first and every time, or there would be no wasps. Science cannot explain this mystery, and yet it cannot be attributed to chance. The wasp covers a hole in the earth, departs cheerfully, and dies. Neither she nor her ancestors have reasoned out the process, nor does she know what happens to her offspring or that there are such things as offspring. She doesn't even know that she has worked and lived her life for the preservation of the race. Bees and ants seem to understand how to organize and govern themselves. They have their soldiers and workers and slaves and drones. If you should pick up a piece of amber on the shore of the Baltic Sea, it might contain an ant imprisoned untold ages ago. You will find it is an almost exact replica of an ant existing today. Did evolution cease when the ant was adjusted to its surroundings in nature? Was the little brain of the ant too small an instrument to meet a higher purpose? Certainly, the ant as a socialized insect had learned much. It seems to apply the wonderful theory of "the greatest good for the greatest number" in a grim way and to carry it to its logical conclusion, as did some natives of the East Indies of the last generation. In some species, the workers bring in little seeds to feed the other ants through the winter. The ants establish what is known as the grinding room, in which those which have developed gigantic jaws especially built for grinding prepare the food for the colony. This is their sole occupation. When the fall comes and the seeds are all ground, "the greatest good for the greatest number" requires that the food supply be conserved, and as there will be plenty of grinders in the new generation, the soldier ants kill off the grinders, satisfying their entomological conscience by believing perhaps that the grinders had had reward enough in having had first chance at the food while they ground.

Certain ants, by means of instinct or reasoning (choose which you prefer), cultivate mushrooms for food in what may be called mushroom gardens, and capture certain caterpillars and aphids (plant lice). These creatures are the ants' cows and goats, from which they take certain exudations of a honeylike nature for food. Ants capture and keep slaves. Some ants, when they make their nests, cut the leaves to size, and while certain workers hold the edges in place, use their babies, which in the larval stage are capable of spinning silk, as shuttles to sew them together. The poor baby may be bereft of the opportunity of making a cocoon for himself, but he has served his community.

How do the inanimate atoms and molecules of matter composing an ant set these complicated processes in motion? There must be Intelligence somewhere.

Only in man has a brain developed to such an extent that he can exercise a high reasoning power. Instinct is like a single note of a flute, beautiful but limited; whereas the human brain contains all the notes of all the instruments in the orchestra. Man can co-ordinate these tones and give to the world symphonies of thought which approach the marvelous. Until man's creation, Providence had not brought a living creature out of primeval rocks which had a brain as flexible as that of man. We can now contemplate the possibility of man's receiving a spark of the Universal Intelligence which makes him supreme on earth, marvelous in his abilities, and immortal in his destiny.

Evolution must, by every law of chemistry and physics, confine its ultimates to the greatest possible fitness to environment; it can go no further. The beauty of a bird's plumage is declared to be a manifestation of sex attraction and thus can be accounted for, but a beautiful painting is not necessary for man's existence, though a beautiful woman may be. Matter as atoms, rocks, or water may combine, and if given life, may evolve into a man; but can these elements, having brought about perfect adaptation to physical environment, go further and produce a musician who can write notes on paper, memorize their beautiful relationship, build a piano, entrance an audience, and have his performance recorded on synthetic plastic discs and sent around the world by a broadcasting station through a medium called ether, about which atoms know nothing except that they exist in it or of it?

Some animals co-ordinate their efforts; they must hunt in packs; they gather food and store it for the future, and in many ways multiply their individual efforts by united action, but beyond this they seem not to go.

Man, on the other hand, built the pyramids by the multiplication of individual strength, but he also discovered the lever, the pulley, the wheel, and fire. He has domesticated the beasts of burden and added his wheel, thus lengthening his legs and strengthening his back. He has conquered the power of falling water, of steam, of gases, and of electricity—turning manual labor into the mere control of mechanisms which are children of his brain. His passage from place to place outstrips the speed of the antelope, and by giving wings to his chariot, he outflies the birds. Has all this come about through a chance interaction of matter?

Beauty seems inherent in all nature. The beauty of the clouds, the rainbow, the blue sky, the exquisite delight that comes to one who looks at the stars, the rising moon, the setting sun, and the spectacular glory of mid-day is an inspirational thrill. Under the microscope the smallest animal and the tiniest flower are elaborately adorned by lines of beauty. The crystalline lines of the elements and compounds, from the snowflake to infinitely smaller forms, are so marvelously true that the artist can only imitate or combine them. Every leaf of every healthy tree is perfectly shaped, and the outline of every plant is fraught with individual character and the lines of true art. The flowers are shaped with grace and perfect adaptations. Their outlines are in true designs, the coloring is delightfully distributed and seldom, if ever, clashes.

A perfect animal is a thing of beauty, and its motions are full of ease and grace. Where a creature has been developed through necessary adjustment to environment and protection and seems incongruous, it becomes so unique that it appears to the onlooker as an artistic expression of the grotesque. The green valley, the river, the arching trees, the cliffs, and the snow-capped mountains cause deep emotions. There is joy in the vast expanse of the curved sand dunes of the desert. The majestic roll of the ocean waves, the breaking of the ground swell on the shore, the flight of birds, whether it be at sea or along the shore or in the jungle with their adapted colorings challenge the one who has the eye to see and the brain to appreciate. The motions of fish, the smooth waving of seaweeds beneath the surface sway one's mind with a sense of rhythm that answers a longing. Nature undistorted appears designed to call forth that which is highest within us, and inspire us with admiration for the Supreme Intelligence which seems to have given us the gift of beauty comprehended in its completeness only by man. Beauty lifts man alone closer to his Creator.

Purpose seems fundamental in all things, from the laws that govern the universe to the combinations of atoms which sustain our lives, and even if there is no other object in evolution than the preparation of a material basis for the reception of spirit, that is an astounding purpose in itself. If the reality of purpose is accepted as to all things, and we believe that man is the present most important manifestation of that purpose, then the scientific belief that man's body and the mechanism of his brain are material may be perfectly sound. Atoms and molecules in living creatures do marvelous things and build wonderful mechanisms, but such machines are useless unless intelligence sets them in objective motion. There is the directive Intelligence which science does not explain, nor does science dare say it is material. Is Intelligence an illusion?

# X

## *Genes*

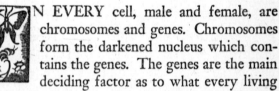N EVERY cell, male and female, are chromosomes and genes. Chromosomes form the darkened nucleus which contains the genes. The genes are the main deciding factor as to what every living thing or a human being shall be. The cytoplasm is the extraordinary chemical combinations which surround them both. The genes are so infinitesimal that if all of them which are responsible for all the human beings on earth today, with their individuality, psychology, color, and race, could be collected and put in one place, there would be less than a thimbleful. These ultra-microscopic genes are the absolute keys to all human, animal, and vegetable characteristics. A thimble is a small place in which to put all the individual characteristics of two billions of human beings. However, the facts are beyond question. Do these genes and cytoplasms lock up all the normal heredity of a multitude of ancestors and preserve the psychology of each in such a tiny space? What is locked up? A book of instructions? An array of atoms? Or is everything left to chance? The embryo recapitulating in its progressive development from

protoplasm to racial identity indicates recorded history retained and expressed by atomic arrangement in the genes and cytoplasm. Even the mother of the child who has nurtured it since conception has little influence, for the genes determine whether the child shall resemble the father or mother, and there is no evidence that this resemblance is determined by its prenatal environment. Evolution usually requires long periods of time for any change to be established. It is a process designed to bring about the survival and identity of the race. Its perfection will be the advent of spirit. It has been devised by the Supreme Intelligence and He will not intervene or hasten it because man does not understand or is impatient. New developments depend upon existing characteristics and a consistent environment. Chance and accident thus have little part in evolution except in bi-parental differences, which are limited to the then inheritable variations.

If you start with a butterfly, you get a caterpillar. The caterpillar eats voraciously, grows to maturity, and wraps itself comfortably in a coat partly of silk and then becomes a chrysalis. Most of the bodily tissues dissolve into cells and become a mixture. No analyst has discovered that one part is different from the other, nor can he separate the mixture. At the proper time every living cell in the chrysalis seeks its proper relationship, and the chrysalis changes into a new creature having life and all the physical organs necessary for existence and the power to reproduce one-half of the complex nature of a new caterpillar.

In due course, the chrysalis opens and there comes into the world a magnificent creature known as a butterfly. Its delicate wings are made up of tubes, into which it pumps its blood. The wing swells and becomes a means of flight, and when the butterfly takes to the air in all its brilliant colors, we find under the microscope that its wings are covered with feather-like scales, and that every spot of red or brown or green or yellow is in the same place that it was on the original butterfly. Its markings are identical with its parents' in every respect, almost to a microscopic scale. What is this directive power of the genes? They control the cells, and the cells obey with the same precision as soldiers. The result is as accurate in general detailed duplication as the solution of a problem in mathematics.

Color is said to arise from the fact that certain substances absorb all the rays of certain wave lengths, leaving the rest to be reflected. Light waves are relatively very big, for they run from thirty-three thousand up to sixty-six thousand to one inch, while other waves or rays run from miles for the radio to ten millions per inch or more for X-rays, radium. And we do not know what else we will discover. Certain tropical butterflies have their wings covered by scales made up partly of excessively thin sheets of a transparent substance. The light penetrates and is reflected in a beautiful blue such as you sometimes see among the colors of an opal. A change of a ten thousandth of an inch in the thickness of the film in the butterfly's wing covering and the color would be different or gone entirely. The genes arrange matters so that for a thousand generations there is no change.

Man can change the genes by using radium and other rays, and this brings about wingless flies, distorted plants, and many astonishing abnormalities, and the scientist may some day improve on nature. In the meantime, however, he is gaining valuable knowledge which will advance biology, medicine and physics.

It is now known that all life comes from a single cell and that there is no evidence to support any other conclusion. It has been observed that all the great groups of living things are separated by gaps that cannot be bridged. Even closely related animals separate, and many soon lose the power of cross-breeding. The offspring of a jackass and a mare is a mule, but there can be no race of mules. As we go back closer and closer to the original source of life, we find adaptation to environment more and more common and one can at least visualize a time when the power of adaptation was complete and the earth, then much as it is now, became populated with living things, "each of its kind." The clam and the octopus are both mollusks, but the separation by adaptive adjustments is almost unbelievable.

As these separations took place in the beginnings of life each creature became more and more specialized and lost the power to turn back or readily readjust himself. Because of this growing inflexibility, vast races became extinct, while general life was still possible for others.

Man is a primate and has a structure like the simian's, but this skelatal resemblance is not necessarily evidence that we are descended from simian ancestors, or that the simians are degenerated descendants from man. No one would claim that the cod evolved from the haddock, though both inhabit the same waters, eat the same food, and have bones that are almost identical. It simply means that somewhere back in the beginning of adaptation there was a parallel necessity for adjustment. Science points to the human thumb of man and its power to grasp and hold tools and weapons as the source of man's advance. The useless thumb of the ape seems conclusive evidence that man's thumb could not have come from the specialized thumb of the tree-living simians, for nature never restores a lost facility. A horse now running on one highly specialized toe can never recover those he has lost. However, we need not concern ourselves too seriously with what occurred to our respective ancestors at least two million generations ago. It seems, however, that the search for the "missing link" is likely to prove futile.

By cross-breeding apparently seemingly new creatures are deliberately developed, such as the greyhound, the Pekinese and the pug. They are all dogs, and if carefully bred true so as to continue emphasis on their acquired characteristics they will remain what they are. If returned to a state of nature, these carefully bred dogs would ultimately revert back to the original type, perhaps a wolf. If, however, they were especially well adapted to the environment in which they found themselves, and could not cross-breed, they would survive as a new species of dog.

Pigeons have been bred to new types almost since history began—fantails, pouters—freaks and maybe crackpots—but the genes are quietly waiting in ambush to return them to the original type. You can see them on the way back to the original on any city street, where you will notice the identical markings and the general tendency to ultimate uniformity in color. We resent half-breeds instinctively, and the cow with five legs, or two heads, horrifies us, but we admire the handsome man, unless he visibly lacks character, and the beautiful woman, but the most beloved of all is a devoted mother.

Genes are part of the sex cells, but sex cells do not take part in general body building, but are segregated and do not participate in any of the less important activities of living things. These cells preserve the complete identity of the race. They seem not to be influenced by the behavior of the parent, except that bad character, disease, or accident may give them very poor materials to work with. A strong pair may have strong children, but this is because there were strong ancestors. Parents may give a child a physical temple to live in or a sewer, which is no place for an immortal soul. Parenthood is man's greatest responsibility.

Men grow no shorter beards because they shave. Tailless cats did not develop on the Isle of Man because someone cut off a cat's tail. No, somehow a tail gene was lost to these cats, and yet, in spite of this disaster, the subsequent cats, without this gene, bred true. Environment does slowly make changes in the relative activities of the genes, and if the change is advantageous these modifications persist; if not, the changed creature is eliminated because it is unfitted to meet the conditions. A Mexican hairless dog might breed true in the Arctic, but his breed would die of cold.

The evolutionists did not know about genes and are left standing where evolution really begins, at the cell, the entity which holds and carries the genes.

How a few million atoms locked up as an ultra-microscopic gene can absolutely rule all life on earth is still one of the greatest marvels of science.

The mystery of which came first, the hen or the egg, is solved forever. It was neither the one nor the other. It was a primordial cell. The egg is merely food for the embryo; it contains this single cell which has met its mate. When the genes in the cells combine and divide, these genes and cytoplasm are now compelled to produce a hen to lay another egg.

Matter, as such, is purposeless; there is no objective even in its obvious obedience to law, but in all organized matter life has a definite project—to build a tree, a vine, an elephant, or a man, in strict accordance with an established design determined by the genes.

Life compels procreation, that the race may be preserved, an impulse so strong that every creature makes its greatest sacrifice for this purpose. With some species, for example, May flies, vast numbers of individuals die at once when they have completed this task.

This compelling force is not found where life is absent. Whence do these masterful impulses arise, and having arisen, why do they persist for millions of years? It is a law of animate nature, as potent as those governing chemical combinations. It comes from above.

The underlying and fundamental differences between all elemental substances of Mother Earth and those which have life, is that while all elements may combine, crystallize, and change in appearance, there is no change in atoms and no conscious relationship. In contrast, living things arrange all the elements in a multitude of new combinations, each in its field of action, vying with the others in its efforts for the preservation of this living relationship. This inherent and active co-operation is entirely absent except where life is present. It has not been accounted for, and yet is as much a law as the law of gravity and must come from the same source. Such laws are part of the universal intelligent order and not an emanation from chaos.

We have found that genes are recognized to be submicroscopic arrangements of the atoms in the sex cells of all things that have life. They hold the design, ancestral record and characteristics of each living thing. They control in detail root, trunk, leaf, flower and fruit of every plant as exactly as they determine the shape, scales, hair, wings of every animal, including man.

An acorn falls to the ground—its tough brown shell holds it safe. It rolls into some earthy crevice. In the spring the germ awakes, the shell bursts, food is provided by the egglike kernel in which the genes were hidden. They send the roots into the earth, and behold a sprout, a sapling, and in years a tree. The germ with its genes has multiplied by trillions and made the trunk, bark, and every leaf and acorn identical with that of the oak which gave it birth. For hundreds of years in each of the countless acorns is preserved the exact arrangement of atoms that produced the first oak tree millions of years ago.

No oak tree ever bore chestnuts. No whale ever gave birth to a fish. The waving fields of wheat are, in every grain, wheat. And corn is corn. Law governs the atomic arrangement in the genes, which absolutely determine every genus of life from beginning to extinction.

Haeckel said "Give me air, water, chemicals and time and I will create a man." He left out the genes and life itself. He would have to find and arrange the invisible atoms and genes and give them life. Even then his chance would be millions to one that he would develop an unheard-of monster. If he did succeed he would declare it was no accident but the result of his intelligence.

Verily "God moves in mysterious ways his wonders to perform."

# XI

## *The World's Greatest Laboratory*

OOKS have been written on the physiology of digestion, but every year brings discoveries of so startling a nature that the subject is ever new. If we think of digestion as a process in a chemical laboratory and of the food that we eat as raw materials, we immediately discover that it is a wonderful process which will digest almost anything edible except the stomach itself.

First into this laboratory we put a variety of food as a raw material without the slightest regard for the laboratory or how the chemistry of digestion will handle it. We eat steak, cabbage, corn, and fried fish, wash it down with any quantity of water, and top it off with alcohol, bread, and beans. We may add sulphur and molasses as spring medicine. Out of this mixture the stomach selects those things which are useful by breaking down into its chemical molecules every item of food, discarding the waste, and reconstructs the residue into new proteins, which become the food of the various cells. The digestive tract selects calcium, sulphur, iodine, iron and any other substances which are necessary, takes care that the essential molecules are not lost, that the hormones can be produced and that all of the vital necessities of life are on hand in regulated quantities, ready to meet every necessity. It stores fat and other reserves to meet such an emergency as starvation, and does all this in spite of human thought or reason. We pour this infinite variety of substances into this chemical laboratory with almost total disregard of what we take in, depending on what we consider the automatic process to keep us alive. When these foods have been broken down and are again prepared, they are delivered constantly to each of our billions of cells, a greater number than all the human beings on earth. The delivery to each individual cell must be constant, and only those substances which the particular cell needs to transform them into bones, nails, flesh, hair, eyes, and teeth are taken up by the proper cell. Here is a chemical laboratory producing more substances than any laboratory which human ingenuity has devised. Here is a delivery system greater than any method of transportation or distribution the world has ever known, all being conducted in perfect order. From childhood until, say, a man is fifty years of age, this laboratory makes no serious mistakes, though the very substances with which it deals could literally form over a million different kinds of molecules—many of them deadly. When the channels of distribution become somewhat sluggish from long use we find weakened ability and ultimate old age.

When the proper food is absorbed by each cell, it

is still only the proper food. The process in each cell now becomes a form of combustion, which accounts for the heat of the whole body. You cannot have combustion without ignition. Fire must be lighted, and so nature provides a little chemical combination which ignites a controlled fire for the oxygen, hydrogen, and the carbon in the food in each cell, thus producing the necessary warmth and, as from any fire, the result is water vapor and carbon dioxide. The carbon dioxide is carried away by the blood to the lungs, and there it is the one thing that makes you draw in your breath of life. A person produces about two pounds of carbon dioxide in a day, but by wonderful processes gets rid of it. Every animal digests food, and each must have the special chemicals it individually needs. Even in minute detail the chemical constituents of the blood, for instance, differ in each species. There is, therefore, a special formative process for each.

In case of infection by hostile germs, the system also continuously maintains a standing army to meet, and usually overcome, invaders and save the entire structure of the man from premature death. No such combination of marvels does or can take place under any circumstances in the absence of life. And all this is done in perfect order, and order is absolutely contrary to chance. Is there Intelligence here? If so, it is due to life. And what is life?

# XII

## *Checks and Balances*

OW strange is the system of checks and balances which has prevented any animal, no matter how ferocious, how large, or subtle, from dominating the earth since the age of trilobites and probably not then. Man only has upset this balance of nature by moving plants and animals from place to place, and he has immediately paid a severe penalty in the development of animal, insect, and plant pests.

A striking illustration which will point out specifically the importance of recognizing these checks in connection with the existence of man is the following fact. Many years ago a species of cactus was planted in Australia as a protective fence. The cactus had no insect enemies in Australia and soon began a prodigious growth. The march of the cactus persisted until it had covered an area approximately as great as England, crowded the inhabitants out of the towns and villages, and destroyed their farms, making cultivation impossible. No device which the people discovered could stop its spread. Australia was in danger of being overwhelmed by a silent, uncontrollable, advancing army of vegetation. The entomologists scoured the world and finally found an insect which lived exclusively on cactus, would eat nothing else, would breed freely, and which had no enemies in Australia. Here the animal conquered the vegetation and today the cactus pest has retreated, and with it all but a small protective residue of the insects, enough to hold the cactus in check forever.

The checks and balances have been provided, and have been persistently effective. Why has not the malarial mosquito so dominated the earth that our ancestors through the ages have not either died or become immune? The same may be said of the yellow fever mosquito, which lived one season as far north as New York. Mosquitoes are plentiful in the Arctic. Why has not the tsetse fly evolved so that he would live in other than his tropical surroundings and wipe out the human race? One has but to mention the plagues and the deadly germs against which man has had no protection until yesterday, and his total lack of knowledge of sanitation as an animal, to understand how wonderful has been his preservation.

Fish and insects survive by meeting the law of chance with thousands of eggs, some of which escape the death that lurks everywhere for the undefended. These strange facts of nature are worth mentioning, although not necessarily conclusive of the existence of the Divine Providence. But man has survived, and one might say, so has the mollusk, but man needed many more protective adjustments and they have been provided.

The insects have no lungs such as man possesses,

but breathe through tubes. When insects grow large
the tubes cannot grow in ratio to the increasing size
of the body of the insect. Hence there never has been
an insect more than inches long and a little longer
wing spread. Because of the mechanism of their structure and their method of breathing, there never could
be an insect of great size. This limit in their growth
held all insects in check and prevented them from
dominating the world. If this physical check had not
been provided, man could not exist. Imagine a primitive man meeting a hornet as big as a lion or a spider
equally large.

Little has been said regarding the many other marvelous adjustments in the physiology of animals, without
which no animal, or indeed vegetable, could continue to exist. These facts are of such extreme importance, however, that they should be mentioned. The
world has recently awakened to the fact that there are
such things as vitamins. The absence of these vitamins cause pellagra, beriberi, scurvy, and what are
known as deficiency diseases. Man must have gone
for millions of years without being aware of these
elusive substances which are necessary to his survival.
Because long voyages without proper diet led to
scurvy and the discovery that lime juice was a cure,
the sailors on great ships of old were called "lime
juicers." The older voyagers did not know the cause
of scurvy. The simple remedy was discovered by
Vasco da Gama when his sailors were dying in Mada-
gascar. It took a century or more before the connection between citrus fruits and the absence of scurvy

was discovered and this deadly disease was banished from the high seas. It took a century or so more to teach man the value of vitamins in citrus fruits, but he did not then learn what the fruit contained. Man also existed for millions of years before he learned the functions of the little chemical laboratories known as the endocrine glands, which supply him with the absolutely essential chemical combinations which they manufacture and which dominate his activities. In addition, these substances that are so potent that one part in a billion will produce profound effects are so adjusted that *they regulate, check and balance each other*. It is well known that when these marvelously complex secretions become unbalanced they create mental and physical distortion of the gravest character. If this disaster should become general civilization would cease and the human race would be reduced to the state of animals, if indeed it survived at all. Placing emphasis however only on those checks, balances and controls without which life as we know it would cease to exist, we are confronted by man's survival with a mathematical problem worth grave consideration by the advocates of chance.

# XIII

## *Time*

HE conscious knowledge of the existence of time is possessed solely by animal life; man alone measures it. The elements which compose all material things rarely change throughout eternity. Combination of elements may occur or separate, but time, while essential to the completion of a chemical change, has no significance to the atoms. A stick of dynamite changes from a solid to a gas in a twenty-five-thousandth of a second, but the atoms are unchanged.

A mountain may arise and be eroded, but a molecule imprisoned in its midst does not anxiously await the time when the rock will disintegrate and set it free, though its electrons spin about their orbits eternally. Your camera snaps at one-hundredth of a second, and eighteen hundred miles of vibration in the ether of space has rushed in to bring about the chemical change. The films thus record in color all the beauties of the scene. The atoms are shaken and rearranged but not otherwise changed.

Living things seem to measure time, but inanimate things only record it. Waters from the melting glaciers of the Ice Age left stratified clay that indicates each year separately, and in a crude way tells the temperature ranges that prevailed. The stalactites and stalagmites of the caves do the same for a hundred thousand years and more, but they know not what they do.

Radium and lead change their proportions in the solid rocks and tell of a billion years of earthly stability and think not of the past. To all living organisms time is inexorable, for life has its span and the individual ceases to be. No living thing in a state of nature consciously measures time, but time measures all living things and masters their activities from birth to the end.

It has been discovered that there is such a thing as biological time. Time for children seems to move slowly. Time for old folks seems to move with great rapidity. This well-known phenomenon has been found to be based upon the life cycle of the cells. Perhaps this can be expressed in the simplest way by saying that the cells of every living creature develop more rapidly at the beginning of life, and slow down toward the end. Biologically speaking, the large number of cell events which occur in childhood gives the child an instinctive impression of a long time, whereas owing to the slower action of the cells in age, it would seem that time passes very swiftly. Life cycles seem to have no relation to absolute time which we measure by the movements of the heavenly bodies. A microbe may reproduce its kind in an hour. Man in so many years. A Mayfly can have no measurement of time beneath the water, but each generation flies its happy lifetime hour beneath the sun. Is it possible that the scientists are right, and that we, if we attain immortality, will measure time by events, and not by astronomy?

The fish of the sea have their time for spawning, but they only obey a law of nature and know not why. Seed time and harvest have their schedule and acres of wheat will ripen almost on the same day. Trees must live so many years to bear fruit, and their annual rings record their age.

It has been found that certain crickets chirp at so many chirps per minute in relation to the temperature. These chirps have been carefully counted and found to record the temperature accurately to within two degrees. A cricket timed for eighteen days began his song of love or joy each day within five minutes of the original hour selected. Certain ducks in a canal in Europe came regularly to a bridge for food each day at a given hour and ring a bell arranged for them. The birds have their time for flight south, and individually decide to join the local flock, and they depart almost to a day each year. Mayflies come out of the lakes for their nuptial flight, and millions strew the streets dead on the same day.

The seventeen-year locusts in New England leave their burrows beneath the earth, where they have lived in darkness, with only slight changes in temperature, and appear by the millions in May of their seventeenth year. A few stragglers, of course, are belated but the vast numbers mature after all these years of darkness, and, with no precedent to guide them, time their appearance almost to a day.

The inch worm humps himself along with great regularity from place to place, and could he count, might measure time and distance as so many humps. But he has no use for mathematics. Don't laugh at his hump, for we civilized humans measure distances by the foot.

All life generally keeps time and records it by action, but of conscious timing shows no evidence. The seasons, the temperature, day and night, and the tides seem to control life's sequences. Evolution has developed habits of unconscious time measurements which apparently operate automatically, as the beating of the heart or digestion. Many people accustomed to awaking at a certain hour, can do so without the aid of an alarm clock, and irrespective of the time they retire. Man has added time to timeless matter; it cannot be weighed nor analyzed. For us time relates to this earth alone, and our measurements may have no relation to the universe as a whole; but it dictates unconscious impulses so strong that it dominates every living thing.

Man, as an animal, has no special sense of time, but he can somewhat control the effect of time on his impulses. Primitive man cannot tell his age except by comparison with events. To him numbers mean only few or many. Modern man forgets his anniversaries, but his wife does not. Is woman more highly evolved, or does she slyly watch the calendar? Neither he nor she could, like the locust, pick out the twenty-fourth day of May after seventeen years in darkness.

Early man loved time as rhythm, as in the even beats of the drum or the tom-tom. The timing in his dances lifted him above instinct. The perfect unison of musical notes has led us to the exquisite thrill of the master harmonies and rhythms of the orchestra. Vibrations in unison at intervals of time, however, is music apparently to man alone.

Civilization has brought to man the necessity for the more accurate and minute measure and record of time. The recurring seasons marked by the time the sun appeared furthest north and south of the equator led to the building of the Druid circles, pyramids, and other time markers throughout the world, and the sun's appearance over these objects or its shadow at a certain mark, usually secret, told the priest how many days to count to planting time or to foretell the flood of the Nile. Now the imperfect calendar hangs in every home, and by this we distinguish the days.

Beyond this, we now record the hours and minutes, the seconds, and the thousandths of a second. The closer we come to accurate time, the more knowledge of chemistry, of physics, of metals, of temperature, and of astronomy we need. Mathematics and still higher mathematics are essential. We calculate the time schedule of the planets, the moons, the comets, and count upon our knowledge of time to predict their movements and to give the hour and the minute of the eclipses, past and present. We know the speed of light per second and note the idiosyncracies of heavenly bodies, which correct themselves in sequence to apparently eternal accuracy.

Evolution has carried living things to an approximate adjustment with the existing environment, but, in theory at least, can go no farther. The advance of man beyond the necessities of existence to a comprehension of time lifts him out of the limits apparently set by physical evolution as a thing apart. As he approaches a complete understanding of time, he also approaches an understanding of some of the eternal laws of the universe and an apprehension of the Supreme Intelligence.

Unless there be intelligent life elsewhere in the universe, man alone knows time, and his mastery of time brings him close to something greater than the material.

Whence comes this mighty leap of man out of chaos, out of all combinations of matter, out of all other living things? It must come from something higher, and not by chance.

# XIV

## *A Perfected Imagination*

LET us leave science for a moment and exercise our imagination.

It may be assumed, that all animals see facts, events and material substances as they are, and that their mental reactions are direct. Their reaction is an attempt to seize food, to flee from an enemy, hide from danger, or to rest comfortably in a place of safety. It is possible that some highly advanced animals, a dog for instance, may dream, and this is, of course, a type of imagination but is without control.

Imagination is one of man's most remarkable faculties. In imagination he can travel instantly where he will. An orator can transport an audience with him. If in his imagination he describes an East Indies atoll, he mentally sees such an island, and his audience also sees an encircling coral reef, the coral strand, the color changes of the open ocean, the sky above, the wind-blown palm trees, and a central island clothed in luxurious tropical foliage. He may describe the limpid lagoon, blue as heaven, mirror-like, and if he carries his thoughts farther, his listener can look into the lagoon's depths.

From this tropic scene the orator can instantly transport his hearers to the blue, green and white of a slow-moving glacier, and call attention to the snow-capped mountain which rises behind, glowing in the rose-tinted beauty of sunrise.

He can take you to a distant star, and almost bring to your ears the clash of the flying elements, or almost make one see and feel the rush of light and heat speeding to warm and give life to an earth and to show its inhabitants the exquisite picture of a crescent moon shining through the darkened green of a forest.

He can bring to your mind not only your own surroundings but your imagined picture of the actual activities of your wife and children at that moment. Here imagination fails. It is imperfect and the actual picture may not by any means be the imagined one.

This power of imagination in a child is a source of great happiness; it is used freely in play: witness the childish belief in play companions. The boy who marches with a wooden gun may well believe he is a soldier.

Education, experience, environment and skill may transform a masterpiece of imagination into a work of art—a play, a symphony, a painting, or an ingenious mechanism. Ideas are the children of the imagination and are thus the foundations of genius. The greatest achievements of the human mind—invention, mechanics, and the startling projection of our minds into higher mathematics—become the ultimate verification of imaginative ideas.

The imagination is, however, constantly handicapped by its material environment, and is therefore only approximately accurate until verified by observation or experience or discovery. Even in our material mind, however, imaginative thought gives no consideration to the idea of time or distance. It reaches its destination—be it a star or your child—instantly.

We must inevitably reach the conclusion that the power of imagination is closely akin to the spiritual. If there is immortality for the spirit, there is immortality for imagination.

Whenever the great philosophers have recognized that highest element in man's nature, the activity of his soul, they have been confronted with difficulties which would not occur to the less thoughtful. If they assume that the spirit is immortal, they find it hard to give this immortal soul a location. The ordinary person, naturally, thinks of heaven as a place, and thinks it as material—the golden streets, the pearly gates. If the destination of a released spirit is heaven, one naturally asks, "Where is heaven and how far is it?" To the mind of the philosopher, whose spirit is awake within him, it must of necessity occur that heaven is not a place in the human sense, but is too marvelous to be grasped by our finite minds, as may be said of infinity itself. Indeed, we may be obliged, by lack of anything in our human experience to guide us, to think that heaven may be space itself.

Naturally, every human being would recoil, almost frigidly, from the idea of being a lonely inhabitant of space. The scientist would awake to the fact that if his spirit wished to reach a point in space, whether a coral island or a distant nebula, the distance to be traveled, whether it be short or long, would take time. If his journey could be accomplished on a beam of light it might take a thousand light years to reach a relatively near-by sun. Therefore, held fast by his material, human relations to inches, miles, light years, and time, it seems to him inconceivable that there could be happiness in blank immeasurable space and eternity.

Here comes in the suggestion of perfected imagination. We on earth are bound to the material and tied to all those material measurements to which reference has been made. However, it must be noted that our imagination, as already stated, instantly overcomes distance, and transports us anywhere, bringing to us inspirations which approach the truth and which open the mind to beauties which outrank the actual. The idea-facts can be materialized and made visible to others, perhaps as an architectural dream, such as the pyramids, the Taj Mahal, or a modern skyscraper. If it be true that the human spirit which has become immortal can see only truth, then through the perfected imagination the spirit will instantly perceive things as they are. Ideas are facts—spiritual facts—which are immortal, whether materialized into a statue, or uttered as a truth which may revolutionize human thought.

The geologist may, in his spiritual imagination, follow the strata of the earth to its molten center. What he sees will be the exact relationship of every element of the earth's crust. The spirit of man can sit quietly on the shore of an atoll, and the breaking sea will sing to him. With his perfected imagination he can watch the billowing gases of the distant sun, and, condensing time, see it from its nebulous beginnings and follow its development until it has cooled and become invisible.

If an immortal spirit can see things as they are, it can acquire all the varied and subtle senses of all living creatures. Thus it can enter into new and amazing fields of knowledge, experience and sensation. It will also, if it desires, see the atoms build themselves into molecules and the molecules destroy the invading bacteria. Perhaps it will enjoy new exquisite music, born of the infinite vibrations of the ether and its thousand octaves. Colors too gorgeous for the human eye await the development of our capacity to comprehend. Unending joyous surprises await the quest of the liberated soul of man.

What may be the limitation of the power of a perfected imagination if attained in the hereafter we cannot know. What checks will protect our sacred right to individual seclusion cannot be discussed here. We are giving here only a mere suggestion. Nor can we attempt to describe the heaven each individual desires, but we can at least assume that the answers to such human questions exist.

Unhindered by time, the immortal spirit can visualize his loved ones, clasp them to his bosom, and as his perfected imagination has now become a spiritual reality, he can see the great truth, known to the children of God, that heaven is wherever he may wish to be.

Let us believe that our imagination will be perfected and that verily the deaf shall hear sounds of beauty beyond human dreams, the dumb shall speak in every language, and the blind shall see every wonder of God's Creation.

As the eternal spirit of man rises Godward, gaining breadth of understanding as it reaches toward the sublime, the wondrous beauty of God's handiwork in the material world fade from sight as do children's stories from the memory of maturity. So indeed does earth sink into insignificance in contemplation of the cosmos. In the glory of spiritual conception, therefore, it may be found that matter is like the shadow that pales before the rising sun and become as nothing.

Within the capacity of his soul, man thus can envision the Divine, and as his spirituality develops, he will come closer to a realization of the majesty, the power, and the glory of his Creator.

# XV

## *A Review*

REVIEW of what has gone before will make evident to the reader that the sole emphasis upon adaptation of nature to man is placed where the absence of this adaptation would make life impossible. It will be found, however, that the other matters given consideration emphasize the remarkable facts in nature which indicate a program for man's development. The evidence is strongly suggestive of this directive purpose back of everything. The goal which seems most reasonable is the creation of intelligent minds. The astounding fact that man has survived the vicissitudes through which he has passed during his millions of years of evolution speaks for itself. We have found that the world is in the right place, that the crust is adjusted to within ten feet, and that if the ocean were a few feet deeper we would have no oxygen or vegetation. We have found that the earth rotates in twenty-four hours and that were this revolution delayed, life would be impossible. If the speed of the earth around the sun were increased or decreased materially, the history of life, if any, would be entirely different. We find that the sun is the one among thousands which could make our sort of life possible on earth, its size, density temperature and the character of its rays all must be right, and are right. We find that the gases of the atmosphere are adjusted to each other and that a very slight change would be fatal. These are but a few of the physical factors which have been brought to the attention of the reader.

Considering the bulk of the earth, its place in space and the nicety of the adjustments, the chances of some of these adjustments occurring is in the order of one to a million and the chances of all of them occurring cannot be calculated even in the billions. The existence of these facts cannot, therefore, be reconciled with any of the laws of chance. It is impossible, then, to escape the conclusion that the adjustments of nature to man are far more amazing than the adjustments of man to nature. A review of the wonders of nature demonstrates beyond question that there are design and purpose in it all. A program is being carried out in all its infinite detail by the Supreme Being we call God. Perhaps one can see in this program a series of events in the development of living things until as its culmination an animal was given life and evolved into man. At all times man seems to have been under the protection, and let us believe, the guidance of the Supreme Being. The program developed in surroundings capable of maintaining a physical creature capable of supporting an adequate brain.

While our minds are finite, we cannot comprehend the infinite. Thus we can only assume a universal intelligence as the basis of all things, including the formation of atoms, planets, suns and nebulæ. Time and space are elements in this conception, and an attempt to personalize such an intelligence baffles the keenest intellect. Nor can we set up man as the only or the ultimate purpose, but we can think of man as one surprising manifestation of this purpose. However, we do not have to understand it all until we develop much further, and accumulating knowledge points toward the ultimate. We do approach the vast abyss of the unknowable when we realize that all matter has scientifically become one by the acceptance of the theory that it is but a manifestation of a universal unit essentially electrical. But certainly chance has little place in the formation of the cosmos, for the mighty universe is governed by law.

The rise of man the animal to a self-conscious reasoning being is too great a step to be taken by the process of material evolution or without creative purpose.

If the reality of purpose is accepted, man as such may be a mechanism. But what operates this mechanism? For without operation it is useless. Science does not account for the operator, nor does Science say that it is material.

Progress has now been sufficient for us to see that God seems to be giving to man a spark of His own intelligence. In a sense, therefore, it seems true that because of this spark we may claim "God made man in his own image." Man is still in his infancy as a creation and is just beginning to sense the advent of what he calls a soul. He is slowly rising to a realization of this gift and instinctively feels its immortality. If this reasoning is true, and the logic seems irrefutable, then this small earth of ours, and perhaps others, takes on a significance undreamed of. So far as we know, our little world has given birth to the first material mechanism to which has been added a part of the Universal Intelligence. This lifts man from animal instinct to reasoning power that can now comprehend the magnificence of cosmos in its implications and dimly sense the true glory of the Supreme Being and His works.

# XVI

## *Chance*

HANCE seems erratic, unexpected and subject to no method of calculation, but though we are startled by its surprises, chance is subject to rigid and unbreakable law. The proverbial penny may turn up heads ten times running and the chance of an eleventh is not expected but is still one in two, but the chance of a run of ten heads is very small. Suppose you have a bag containing one hundred marbles, ninety-nine black and one white. Shake the bag and let out one. The chance that the first marble out being the white one is exactly one in one hundred. Now put the marbles back and start over again. The chance of the white coming out is still one in a hundred, but the chance of the white coming out first twice in succession is one in ten thousand (one hundred times one hundred).

Now try a third time, and the chance of the white coming out three times in succession is one hundred times ten thousand or one in a million. Try another time or two and the figures become astronomical.

The results of chance are as closely bound by law as the fact that two and two make four.

In a game in which the cards are shuffled and an ace of spades was dealt to one of the players, ace of hearts to the next, clubs to the third and diamonds to the dealer, followed by the deuces, the threes and so on, until each player had a complete set in numerical order, no one would believe the cards had not been arranged.

The chances are so great against such a happening that probably it never did happen in all the games played anywhere since whist was invented. "But it could happen." Yes, it could. Suppose a little child is asked by an expert chess player to beat him at chess in thirty-four moves and the child makes each move by pure chance exactly right to meet every twist and turn the expert attempts and does beat him in thirty-four moves. The expert would certainly think it was a dream or that he was out of his mind. "But it could happen." Yes, it could.

To repeat, my purpose in this discussion of chance is to bring forcibly to the attention of the reader the fact that the purpose of this book is to point out clearly and scientifically the narrow limits within which any life can exist on earth, and prove by real evidence that all the nearly exact requirements of life could not be brought about on one planet at one time by chance. The size of the earth, the distance from the sun, the temperature and the life-giving rays of the sun, the thickness of the earth's crust, the quantity of water, the amount of carbon dioxide, the volume of nitrogen, the emergence of man and his survival— all point to order out of chaos, to design and purpose, and to the fact that, according to the inexorable laws of mathematics, all these could not occur by chance simultaneously on one planet once in a billion times. It *could* so occur, but it *did not so occur*. When the facts are so overwhelming, and when we recognize, as we must, the attributes of our minds which are not material, is it possible to flaunt the evidence and take the one chance in a billion that we and all else are the result of chance?

We have found that there are 999,999,999 chances to one against a belief that all things happen by chance. Science will not deny the facts as stated; the mathematicians will agree that the figures are correct. Now we encounter the stubborn resistance of the human mind, which is reluctant to give up fixed ideas. The early Greeks knew the earth was a sphere, but it took two thousand years to convince men that this fact is true.

New ideas encounter opposition, ridicule and abuse, but truth survives and is verified.

The argument is closed; the case is submitted to you, the jury, and your verdict will be awaited with confidence.

# XVII

## *Conclusion*

HE first chapter of Genesis contains the real story of creation, and its essence has not been changed by knowledge acquired since it was written. This statement will cause a smile to develop on the genial face of the scientist and a look of incredulity but satisfaction from the true believer. The differences have arisen over details which are not worth controversy. Let us examine the facts as they are presented in this remarkable first chapter of the Bible:

"In the beginning God created the heaven and the earth. And the earth was without form, and void."

This is the original chaos of an unformed earth.

"Darkness was upon the face of the deep."

The oceans were mostly in the sky, as impenetrable clouds, and no light could reach the earth.

"And God said, Let there be light: and there was light."

The clouds were cleared away. The earth had cooled, the rotation of the earth made night and day.

"God said, Let there be a firmament in the midst of the waters."

Out of the waters which covered all the earth rose the continents, and the dry land appeared, and above the earth, the atmosphere.

"And God said, Let the earth bring forth grass, the herb yielding seed, . . ."

Note that vegetation is mentioned before animal life.

"And God made two great lights. . . . He made the stars also."

The sun and the moon became visible through the clouds and as the clouds finally cleared, the stars appeared, "also."

"And God said, Let the waters bring forth abundantly the moving creature that hath life, and fowl that may fly above the earth in the open firmament of heaven."

All moving life originated in the water, and the firmament of heaven is the atmosphere.

"And God said, Let the earth bring forth the living creature after his kind, cattle, and creeping thing, and beast of the earth."

Animals are now on earth after the seas had been populated.

"And God said, Let us make man in our image, . . . and let them have dominion over every living thing. He blessed them, and said unto them, Be fruitful, and multiply."

All this has come to pass, and man has dominion.

"I have given every green herb for meat."

Here is a statement in biology that is most surprising, considering the time it was made. It is correct and in perfect accord with scientific knowledge. The statement about green herbs was not proved true until the synthesis of chlorophyl was discovered and the fact that all life was dependent on *every green thing* was made known by science. So is the order of procedure from chaos to man and his dominion. Can science pick a flaw in this briefest story ever told? the world's history in a few lines of print? The rest is detail. We must accord our homage to the writer, unknown and unheralded, in complete humility bow to his wisdom and admit his inspiration. In the face of the simple truth here told, let us not quarrel over details due to translation and human interpolation or over the question of how God did His work or the time it took. Who knows? The facts as told have come down through the ages and *are facts.*

We may develop a theory as to how all things having life developed from the original cell, but science stops there. We can agree with the master minds whose painstaking research have given us a real picture of the physical facts of the material world, but are not bound to stop where they stop because they cannot yet see the hand of God. The scientist does not affirm, nor can he deny, the existence of Spirit or a Supreme Intelligence, yet in his inmost self he feels the impact of consciousness, thought, memory, and ideas emanating from that entity we call the soul. He knows his inspiration does not come from matter. Science has no claim or right to the last word on the existence of a Supreme Intelligence until it can speak that word finally and forever.

The fact that man, everywhere at all times, from the beginning to the present day, has felt the impulse to call upon something he believed to be higher and more powerful than himself, shows that religion is innate and should be scientifically recognized. Whether man has endowed a graven image with his feeling that there is an outside power for good or evil is not the important thing. The real fact is his acknowledgment of his Father in heaven. We who have access to the knowledge of the world should not look with scorn at the crudities of those who have gone before or of those who now do not know the truth as we see it. Rather, we should stand in awe, amazement and reverence to see the universality of man's search for, and belief in, a supreme being. Is it not his soul that feels akin to the Supreme Intelligence? Do we fear to assert that the religious impulse found only in man is as much a part of an intelligent being as any other attribute? Its existence is as much an evidence of the purpose of the Supreme Intelligence as is the material but marvelous brain of man, in which resides his sentient being.

No atom or molecule ever had a thought, no combination of the elements ever gave birth to an idea, no natural law ever built a cathedral; but, obedient to certain impulses of life, certain living structures have been made which contain something to which the particles of matter are, in turn, obedient, and we see, as a result, all the wonders of civilization. What is this living structure? Atoms and molecules? Yes. And what else? An intangible something so superior to matter that it dominates all things, and so different from the material of which the world is made that it cannot be seen, weighed or measured. So far as we know, it has no laws to govern it. The soul of man is "master of its destiny" but is conscious of its relation to the supreme source of its existence. For man it has developed a code of ethics which no other animal has or needs. To call this entity an outgrowth of combinations of matter because we do not know by the test tube what it is, begs the question. It exists and manifests itself by its works, by self-sacrifice, by its control of matter, and, above all, by its power to lift material man out of human weakness and error into harmony with the will of the Supreme Being. This is the essence of God's purpose. This accounts for the innate longing of man for contact with things higher than himself. This discloses the basis of his religious impulse. This *is* religion.

Science recognizes and gives full credit to man's craving for higher things, but it does not take seriously the dogmas of the hundred and one jarring creeds, though it does see in them all paths which converge toward God. What science sees, and what all thinking men know, is the unbelievable value of the universal faith in a Supreme Being.

Man's advance to morality and a sense of obligation

is the outgrowth of faith in God and belief in immortality. The richness of religious experience finds the soul of man and lifts him, step by step, until he feels the Divine presence. The instinctive cry of man, "God help me," is natural, and the crudest prayer lifts one closer to his Creator.

Reverence, generosity, nobility of character, morality, inspiration, and what may be called the Divine attributes, do not arise from atheism or negation, a surprising form of self-conceit which puts man in the place of God. Without faith, civilization would become bankrupt, order would become disorder, restraint and control would be lost, and evil would prevail. Let us, then, hold fast to our belief in a Supreme Intelligence, the love of God and the brotherhood of man, lifting ourselves closer to Him by doing His will as we know it and accepting the responsibility of believing we are, as His creation, worthy of His care.

The leaven of ethical progress is slowly but surely bringing man to a better comprehension of his relations to his fellows, and has set ideals to which humanity will ultimately attach itself.

In eternity man's existence on earth is a very short time. His present imperfection is but an incident in his development from merely a chemical structure into what he may ultimately become—pure spirit. The Supreme Being will give us time, and as we progress, we can utter the most sincere prayer of which we are now capable:

Oh, God, lead us along the path of Thy great design. Lift us into spiritual harmony with each other. Give us the ability to become a part of the progress toward spiritual perfection. Lead us into Thy service and thus make us instruments in the execution of Thy will.

MAN DOES NOT STAND ALONE!